D0549791

Test your scientific maths skills with CGP!

Maths is more important than ever in Grade 9-1 GCSE Science, but it can be easy to overlook when you're up to your eyeballs in scientific facts.

Not to worry. This CGP book is packed with bite-sized 10-Minute Tests that'll fit perfectly into your revision timetable. It covers all the maths you'll need for Foundation Level GCSE Science — whichever course you're taking.

To round things off, all the answers are included at the back, along with a chart to keep track of your progress. It's the best way to bag top marks for maths!

CGP — still the best ☺

Our sole aim here at CGP is to produce the highest quality books — carefully written, immaculately presented and dangerously close to being funny.

Then we work our socks off to get them out to you — at the cheapest possible prices.

How to use this book

- There are 30 tests in this book — each one is either biology, chemistry, or physics-based.

- We've given you more physics tests to have a go at than chemistry or biology tests — that's because there are more maths marks available in GCSE physics exam papers than there are in GCSE chemistry or biology exam papers. There are more chemistry tests than biology tests for a similar reason.

- The questions are designed to test your maths skills rather than the scientific knowledge you'll need for the real exams. For this reason, we've given you all the scientific equations you'll need to answer the questions — in the exams, you'll be expected to recall a lot of these.

- Before you start a test, make sure you've got a pen, pencil, calculator and ruler. For some of the physics tests, you'll also need a protractor.

- Each test is worth 8 or 9 marks and should take you roughly 10 minutes to complete.

- We've included full working in the answers for every question — so if you get stuck on a question, you can look up how to do it <u>after</u> you've finished a test. Don't worry if you get the right answer, but use a different method to work it out — you'll still get the marks in the exam.

- The answers also include a mark scheme, so you can see what each mark is awarded for. Just like in the real exams, make sure you write down all your working — if you don't get the right answer, you might still pick up some marks for showing evidence of the correct calculation or method.

- You can use the progress chart on page 71 to record your scores and keep track of how you're doing.

Published by CGP

<u>Editors</u>:
Emily Sheraton, Hayley Thompson and Charlotte Whiteley.

With thanks to Barrie Crowther, Ian Francis and Paul Jordin for the proofreading.

ISBN: 978 1 78294 865 0
Printed by Elanders Ltd, Newcastle upon Tyne
Clipart from Corel®

Based on the classic CGP style created by Richard Parsons.

Text, design, layout and original illustrations © Coordination Group Publications Ltd. (CGP) 2018
All rights reserved.

Photocopying this book is not permitted, even if you have a CLA licence.
Extra copies are available from CGP with next day delivery • 0800 1712 712 • www.cgpbooks.co.uk

Contents

Biology: Test 1

There are **5 questions** in this test. Give yourself **10 minutes** to answer them all.

1. A scientist uses a light microscope to look at the cells in a root tip. He can see 63 cells, two-thirds of which are not dividing. Calculate the number of cells that are not dividing.

    ....

    ....

    .... cells
    [1]

2. Two alleles, N and n, control wing shape in fruit flies.
    'NN' or 'Nn' produce normal wings.
    'nn' produces little wings.

    The squares in the genetic diagram on the right show the possible offspring when two 'Nn' parent flies reproduce. All of the offspring are equally likely.

    If two 'Nn' parents reproduce, what is the probability that the offspring will have little wings? Tick **one** box.

    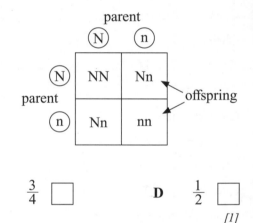

    A $\frac{1}{4}$ ☐   **B** $\frac{1}{3}$ ☐   **C** $\frac{3}{4}$ ☐   **D** $\frac{1}{2}$ ☐
    [1]

3. Beth is 1.50 m tall and has a body mass of 50.4 kg. Calculate her BMI.

    $$BMI = \frac{\text{Body mass (kg)}}{(\text{Height (m)})^2}$$

    ....

    ....

    .... kg/m²
    [2]

© CGP — not to be photocopied

4. Omar is investigating the effect of pH on the activity of the enzyme amylase.
Some of his results are shown in the table below.

pH	2	3	4	5	6
Amylase activity (% of maximum)	20	40	55	65	85

Use the data in the table to complete the graph below. Draw a line of best fit.

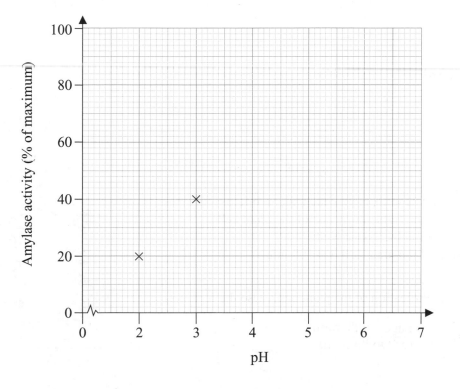

[3]

5. A student measures his reaction time using a computer test. He repeats the same test six times.
His results are shown below. Calculate his mean reaction time to 2 significant figures.

	Repeat 1	Repeat 2	Repeat 3	Repeat 4	Repeat 5	Repeat 6
Reaction time (s)	0.25	0.25	0.26	0.23	0.21	0.25

....

....

.... s

[2]

9

© CGP — not to be photocopied

Biology: Test 1

Biology: Test 2

There are **6 questions** in this test. Give yourself **10 minutes** to answer them all.

1. There are 1 230 000 DNA bases in a section of chromosome.
    Which of the following, **A** to **D**, shows this number written in standard form? Tick **one** box.

    A 12.3×10^5 ☐

    B 1.23×10^{-6} ☐

    C 1.23×10^6 ☐

    D 1.23×10^4 ☐

    [1]

    A student looked at some plant cells under a microscope.
    The diagram on the right shows one of the plant cells.
    In the diagram, A is the image width.
    The real width of the plant cell is 0.108 mm.

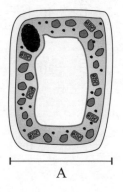

2. What is the magnification of the plant cell? Use the formula:

    $$\text{magnification} = \frac{\text{image width (mm)}}{\text{real width (mm)}}$$

    ....

    ....

    × ....
    [2]

3. 1 mm = 1000 μm. Calculate the real width of the plant cell in μm.

    ....

    .... μm
    [1]

© CGP — not to be photocopied

The graph on the right shows water uptake by a plant over eight hours.

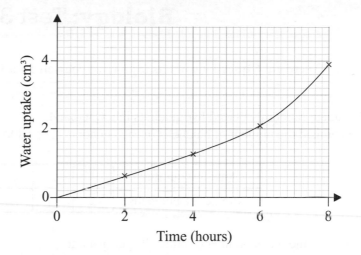

4. Calculate the volume of water taken up by the plant between 2 hours and 6 hours.

....

.... cm³

[1]

5. Use your answer to question 4 and the following formula to calculate the mean rate of water uptake between 2 hours and 6 hours.

$$\text{mean rate of water uptake} = \frac{\text{volume of water taken up}}{\text{time taken}}$$

....

....

.... cm³/hour

[2]

6. The diagram below represents a cell. The height, width and length of the cell are given in micrometres (μm). Which of the following, **A** to **D**, is the surface area of the cell?
Tick **one** box.

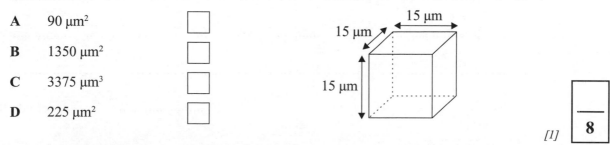

A   90 μm²   ☐

B   1350 μm²   ☐

C   3375 μm³   ☐

D   225 μm²   ☐

[1]

| 8 |

© CGP — not to be photocopied

Biology: Test 2

Biology: Test 3

There are **6 questions** in this test. Give yourself **10 minutes** to answer them all.

A student randomly placed five quadrats in a woodland.
He counted the number of bluebells in each quadrat. The table below shows his results.

Quadrat number	1	2	3	4	5
Number of bluebells	2	12	7	0	9

1. Calculate the mean number of bluebells per quadrat.

    ....

    ....

    .... bluebells
    [1]

2. The student's quadrat had an area of 1 m². The woodland has an area of 4200 m².
    Use this information and your answer to question 1 to estimate the total number of bluebells
    in the woodland.

    ....

    ....

    .... bluebells
    [1]

3. A group of respiring woodlice produce 6.3 cm³ of CO_2 in 54 minutes.
    Calculate their mean rate of CO_2 production per minute. Give your answer to 2 significant figures.

    ....

    ....

    .... cm³/min
    [2]

© CGP — not to be photocopied

4. Peter recorded his pulse rate during four different activities.
His results are shown in the table below.

Activity	sitting	walking	jogging	running
Pulse rate (beats per minute)	68	80	124	136

Use the data in the table to complete the chart below.

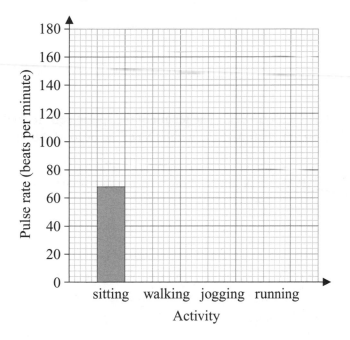

[2]

A scientist counted the number of bacterial colonies in 7 Petri dishes.
Her results are shown in the table below.

5. Give the median number of bacterial colonies.

Petri dish	1	2	3	4	5	6	7
No. of bacterial colonies	27	43	87	27	76	42	77

....

.... bacterial colonies

[1]

6. Give the mode for the number of bacterial colonies.

.... bacterial colonies

[1]

8

Biology: Test 4

There are **6 questions** in this test. Give yourself **10 minutes** to answer them all.

1. A cell has a surface area to volume ratio of 250 : 625. Give this ratio in the form n : 1.

    ....

    .... : 1

    [1]

2. The diagram below shows a sperm cell. The length of the sperm cell (from the tip of the head to the tip of the tail) is 50 μm. Estimate the width (X) of the head of the sperm cell.

    X μm   ....

    .... μm

    [1]

3. A patient has a heart rate of 70 beats/minute, and a stroke volume of 74 cm³/beat.

    cardiac output = stroke volume × heart rate

    Calculate the patient's cardiac output.

    ....

    .... cm³/minute

    [2]

4. A student wants to find out the concentration of the solution inside potato cells. She cuts a cylinder from a potato, then measures its mass before and after placing it in a beaker of sugar solution for 24 hours. The table shows her results.

Mass of potato cylinder (g)	
At the start	After 24 hours
2.0	1.8

    Calculate the percentage change in mass for the potato cylinder.

    ....

    ....

    ....%

    [2]

Biology: Test 4

© CGP — not to be photocopied

5. Another student carried out a similar experiment by placing potato cylinders in different concentrations of sugar solution. He produced the graph on the right.

The point where the line crosses the *x*-axis is equal to the concentration of the solution inside the potato cells.

Find the concentration of the solution inside the potato cells.

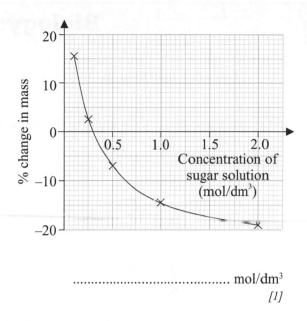

.... mol/dm³

[1]

6. A farmer records the amount of crop produced by his farm every year for 5 years.
The results are shown in the bar chart below.
Calculate how much more crop was produced in Year 1 than Year 3.

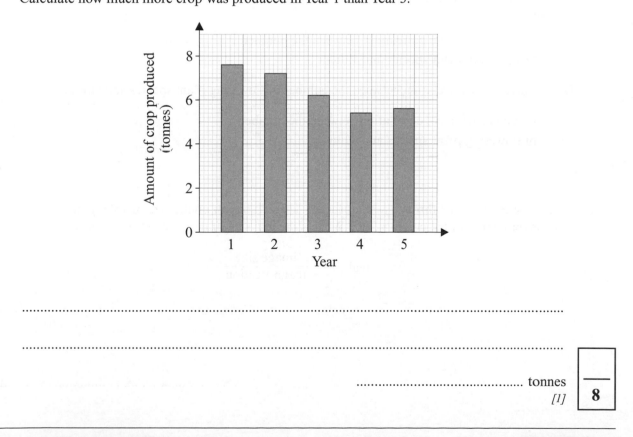

....

....

.... tonnes

[1]

© CGP — not to be photocopied

Biology: Test 4

Biology: Test 5

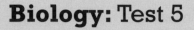

There are **5 questions** in this test. Give yourself **10 minutes** to answer them all.

1. The graph below shows the number of flowering plant species that are found at different altitudes.

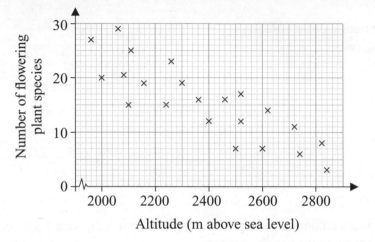

Which of the following statements, **A** to **C**, describes the relationship shown in the graph?
Tick **one** box.

A There is a positive correlation between the number
of flowering plant species and altitude. ☐

B There is no correlation between the number of flowering plant species and altitude. ☐

C There is a negative correlation between the number
of flowering plant species and altitude. ☐

[1]

2. A scientist views a cell through a microscope. The cell has an image size of 1800 µm.
The magnification of the cell is × 200. What is the real size of the cell? Use the formula:

$$\text{real size} = \frac{\text{image size}}{\text{magnification}}$$

....

....

.... µm
[2]

© CGP — not to be photocopied

3. In a food chain, plants take in 9850 kJ/m²/yr of energy from the Sun.
   Herbivores take in 897 kJ/m²/yr of this energy from the plants.
   What percentage of the energy taken in by the plants was then taken in by the herbivores?

   ....

   ....

   ....%
   [2]

4. An enzyme denatures at temperatures > 45 °C. It also denatures at a pH of > 8.8 or < 2.0.
   At a temperature of 39 °C and a pH of 9.2, will the enzyme be denatured?
   Explain your answer.

   ....

   ....
   [1]

5. Sophia was investigating the heights of pea plants in her garden. The grouped frequency
   table below shows her results. How many of Sophia's pea plants are taller than 105 cm?

Height (cm)	Frequency
$70 < h \leq 85$	2
$85 < h \leq 95$	14
$95 < h \leq 100$	10
$100 < h \leq 105$	9
$105 < h \leq 110$	5
$110 < h \leq 120$	1

   ....

   ....

   .... plants
   [2]

8

Section 2 — Chemistry

Chemistry: Test 1

There are **5 questions** in this test. Give yourself **10 minutes** to answer them all.

1. A student adds 13.2 g of potassium chloride (a solute) to 0.44 dm³ of water (a solvent).
    Using the following formula, calculate the concentration of the student's solution:

    $$\text{concentration (g/dm}^3) = \frac{\text{mass of solute (g)}}{\text{volume of solvent (dm}^3)}$$

    ....

    ....

    .... g/dm³

    [2]

2. A combustion reaction produced 144 dm³ of CO_2. Calculate the volume of CO_2 produced in cm³.
    (1 dm³ = 1000 cm³)

    ....

    .... cm³

    [1]

3. The table below shows the volume of water processed by a
    water treatment plant each day over a 3 day period.

	Volume of water processed (dm³)
Day 1	4 490 000
Day 2	4 010 000
Day 3	4 460 000

    Calculate the mean volume of water processed by the plant per day.
    Give your answer in standard form.

    ....

    ....

    .... dm³ per day

    [2]

© CGP — not to be photocopied

The diagram below shows the structural formula for the compound propanol.

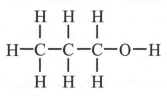

4. Complete the table below for the elements in propanol.

Element	A_r	Number of atoms	$A_r \times$ number of atoms
H	1	8	$1 \times 8 = 8$
C	12	....	....
O	16	....	....

[1]

5. The percentage mass of an element in a compound can be calculated using the following formula:

$$\text{percentage mass of an element in a compound} = \frac{A_r \times \text{number of atoms of that element}}{M_r \text{ of the compound}} \times 100$$

The M_r of propanol is 60.

Use the table you completed in question 4 to calculate the percentage mass of the element O (oxygen) in the compound propanol. Give your answer to 2 significant figures.

....

....

....

.... %

[3]

9

Chemistry: Test 2

There are **5 questions** in this test. Give yourself **10 minutes** to answer them all.

1. A student heats a solution of sodium chloride in an evaporating dish.
    He heats the solution until all the water is removed, leaving only solid sodium chloride.

    Using the information in the table below, calculate the mass
    of solid sodium chloride produced by the student.

Mass of empty evaporating dish (g)	Mass of evaporating dish and contents after heating (g)
25.4	26.2

    ....

    .... g

    [1]

2. 1.5 kg of a steel alloy contains 6 g of carbon. What percentage of the steel alloy is carbon?

    ....

    ....

    .... %

    [2]

3. Niall records how long it takes for a reaction to finish.
    The table below shows his repeat results. The result for Repeat 3 is missing.
    Calculate the time it took for the reaction to finish during Repeat 3.

	Repeat 1	Repeat 2	Repeat 3	Mean
Time (s)	183	180		181

    ....

    ....

    .... s

    [1]

© CGP — not to be photocopied

Meera reacts dilute hydrochloric acid with calcium carbonate.
She measures the volume of carbon dioxide produced over 40 seconds using a gas syringe.
Her results are shown in the table below.

Time (s)	Volume of carbon dioxide produced (cm³)
0	0.00
10	0.20
20	0.38
30	0.62
40	0.84

4. Plot Meera's results on the graph below. Draw a straight line of best fit.

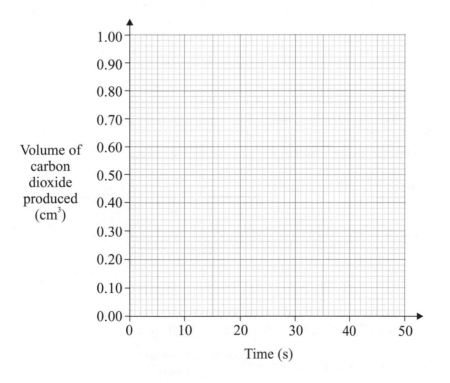

Time (s)

[3]

5. Use your graph to estimate the volume of carbon dioxide produced after 26 seconds.

.... cm³

[1]

8

16

Chemistry: Test 3

There are **5 questions** in this test. Give yourself **10 minutes** to answer them all.

1. The M_r of a compound is calculated by adding up the A_r for each atom in that compound.
    The table below shows the A_r for each of the atoms in magnesium sulfate.

Atom	A_r
Mg	24
S	32
O	16

    Magnesium sulfate ($MgSO_4$) contains 1 Mg atom, 1 S atom and 4 O atoms.
    Use this information and the information in the table to calculate the M_r of magnesium sulfate.

    ....

    $M_r =$..

    [1]

2. A student records the temperature change for a reaction.
    At the start of the reaction, the temperature was 25 °C.
    At the end of the reaction, the temperature was 27 °C.
    Calculate the percentage increase in temperature during the reaction.

    ....

    ....

    ....%

    [2]

3. A reaction takes 250 seconds. 0.200 dm³ of product is made.
    Calculate the mean rate of reaction in cm³/s. (1 dm³ = 1000 cm³)

    $$\text{mean rate of reaction} = \frac{\text{amount of product formed}}{\text{time}}$$

    ....

    ....

    .... cm³/s

    [3]

The table below shows the composition of the waste recycled
by a waste collection facility in 2017.

Material	Percentage by mass of total material recycled (%)
Glass	26
Paper	38
Plastic	13
Metal	19
Other	4

4. Complete the bar chart of this data on the axes below.

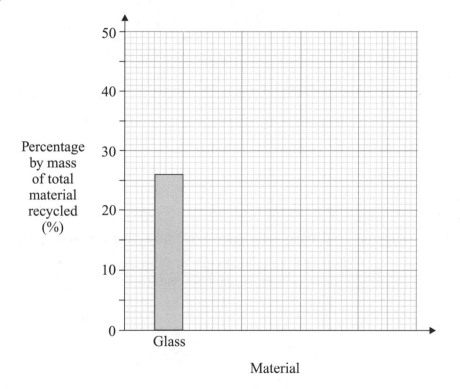

[2]

5. The waste collection facility recycled 1 650 000 kg of waste in 2017.
Using the information in the table, calculate the mass of glass recycled by the facility.

....

.... kg

[1]

9

© CGP — not to be photocopied

Chemistry: Test 4

There are **6 questions** in this test. Give yourself **10 minutes** to answer them all.

The diagram below shows a chromatogram from a chromatography experiment.

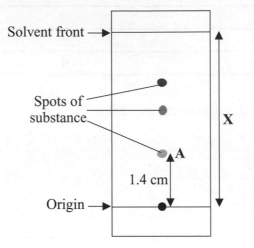

1. Measure the distance, **X**, from the origin to the solvent front.

.... cm

[1]

2. Use your answer to question 1 and the formula below to calculate the R_f value of spot **A**.

$$R_f = \frac{\text{distance from origin to spot of substance}}{\text{distance from origin to solvent front}}$$

....

$R_f =$ ....

[2]

The M_r of a compound can be calculated by adding up the A_r for each atom in that compound. Sodium chloride (NaCl) contains 1 Na atom and 1 Cl atom.

3. Calculate the M_r of sodium chloride. A_r of Na = 23, A_r of Cl = 35.5

....

$M_r =$ ....

[1]

© CGP — not to be photocopied

4. Use your answer to question 3 and the following formula to calculate the percentage mass of sodium (Na) in sodium chloride (NaCl). A_r of Na = 23

$$\text{percentage mass of an element in a compound} = \frac{A_r \times \text{number of atoms of that element}}{M_r \text{ of the compound}} \times 100$$

....

....

.... %

[2]

5. A student reacted zinc ribbon with dilute hydrochloric acid.
She calculated the maximum theoretical yield of zinc chloride to be 2.8 g.
The actual yield of zinc chloride was 2.1 g.
Calculate the percentage yield of zinc chloride.

$$\text{Percentage yield} = \frac{\text{Mass of product actually made}}{\text{Maximum theoretical mass}} \times 100$$

....

....

.... %

[2]

6. The diagram below represents a nanoparticle.
Its height, length and width are given in nanometres (nm).

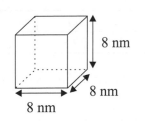

Calculate the volume of the nanoparticle.

....

.... nm³

[1]

9

Chemistry: Test 4

Chemistry: Test 5

There are **5 questions** in this test. Give yourself **10 minutes** to answer them all.

1. The Haber process is used to make ammonia from nitrogen and hydrogen.
    The nitrogen is obtained from the air, which is 78% nitrogen.
    How many cm^3 of nitrogen are there in 24 cm^3 of air?

    ....

    .... cm^3
    [1]

2. A reaction is carried out. The mean rate of this reaction over the first 120 seconds is 0.140 g/s
    Use the formula below to calculate the amount of product that would form after 120 s.

    Amount of product formed = rate of reaction × time

    ....

    .... g
    [2]

3. A student carried out a reaction in an evaporating dish. The reaction produced carbon dioxide gas.
    The student measured the mass of the dish and its contents at the start of the reaction,
    and at 30 second intervals. The table below shows his results.

Time (s)	0	30	60	90	120	150
Mass (g)	34.3	32.0	29.8	29.7	28.8	29.6

    Calculate the percentage decrease in the recorded mass between 30 and 120 seconds.

    ....

    ....

    .... %
    [2]

     © CGP — not to be photocopied

4. The graph below shows how much gas was produced from a reaction in 50 seconds.
    The gradient of the graph is equal to the rate of the reaction.

    Using this information, what are the units for the rate of this reaction?

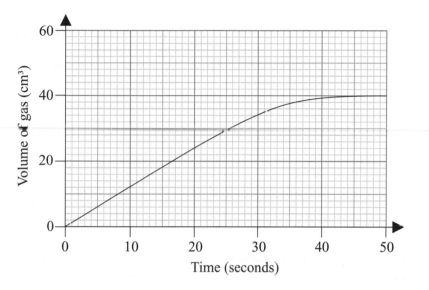

units = ...

[1]

5. A solution of potassium bromide contains 30 g of potassium bromide and 200 cm^3
    of water. Calculate the concentration of the potassium bromide solution in g/dm^3.
    ($1\ cm^3 = 0.001\ dm^3$)

$$\text{Concentration (g/dm}^3) = \frac{\text{mass (g)}}{\text{volume (dm}^3)}$$

....

....

....

.... g/dm^3

[3]

9

Chemistry: Test 6

There are **5 questions** in this test. Give yourself **10 minutes** to answer them all.

1. Copper oxide was reacted with dilute sulfuric acid. The reaction produced 23.4 g of copper sulfate.
    The percentage yield for this reaction was 78.0%. Using the formula below, calculate the
    maximum theoretical mass of copper sulfate that could have been produced in this reaction.

    $$\text{Maximum theoretical mass} = \frac{\text{mass of product actually made}}{\text{percentage yield}} \times 100$$

    ....

    .... g

    [2]

2. The diagram below shows the temperature change of a reaction between zinc and copper sulfate
    solution. Calculate the maximum temperature change for this reaction.

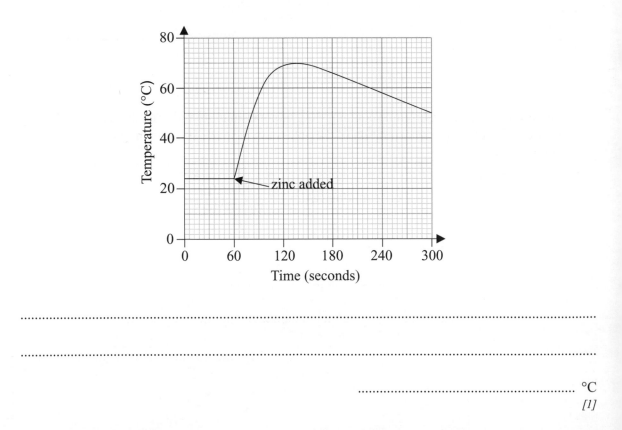

    ....

    ....

    .... °C

    [1]

© CGP — not to be photocopied

3. A solution of sodium hydroxide contains 0.46 dm³ of water. The concentration of the solution is 18 g/dm³. Calculate the mass of sodium hydroxide in this solution. Give your answer to 2 significant figures.

$$\text{Mass (g)} = \text{concentration (g/dm}^3) \times \text{volume (dm}^3)$$

....

....

.... g

[3]

A scientist tested the boiling points of different hydrocarbons.
A frequency table of their boiling points is shown below.

Class — boiling point (°C)	Frequency
$-110 < x \le -70$	1
$-70 < x \le -30$	1
$-30 < x \le 10$	4
$10 < x \le 50$	5
$50 < x \le 90$	2
$90 < x \le 130$	3
$130 < x \le 170$	2

4. Which class of boiling points contains the most hydrocarbons?

....

[1]

5. How many of the hydrocarbons tested had a boiling point greater than 10 °C?

....

....

[2]

9

Chemistry: Test 7

There are **5 questions** in this test. Give yourself **10 minutes** to answer them all.

1. A reaction starts with 50 g of reactants. 2 g of gas is given off.
   Calculate the percentage of the original mass that was lost as gas.

   ....

   ....

   ....%
   [1]

2. The M_r of a compound is calculated by adding up
   the A_r for each of the atoms in that compound.
   The table on the right shows the A_r for each of
   the atoms in calcium carbonate ($CaCO_3$).

Atom	A_r
Ca	40
C	12
O	16

   Calcium carbonate contains 1 Ca atom, 1 C atom and 3 O atoms.
   Use this information and the information in the table to calculate the M_r of calcium carbonate.

   ....

   M_r = ...
   [1]

3. A student carried out a reaction which produced 56 cm³ of product in 40 s.
   Use the formula below to calculate the mean rate of reaction.
   Include the units for the rate in your answer.

   $$\text{mean rate of reaction} = \frac{\text{amount of product formed}}{\text{time}}$$

   ....

   ....

   ....
   [3]

Chemistry: Test 7

© CGP — not to be photocopied

A student recorded the mass of a product that formed over time during a chemical reaction. Her results are shown in the table below.

Time (s)	0	10	20	30	40	50	60
Mass of product (g)	0	1.7	2.9	3.6	4.0	4.2	4.3

4. Use the data in the table to complete the graph below.
   Draw a line of best fit.

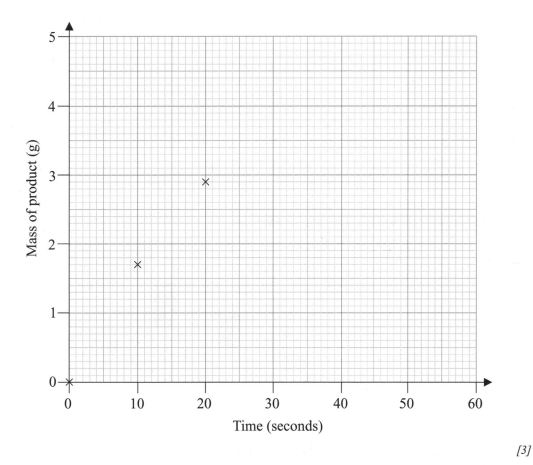

[3]

5. Using the graph above, estimate the time at which 3.3 g of product would have formed.

.... s

[1]

9

Chemistry: Test 8

There are **4 questions** in this test. Give yourself **10 minutes** to answer them all.

1. A student reacted zinc with dilute hydrochloric acid and measured the volume of hydrogen gas produced. She repeated the experiment three times. Her results are shown in the table below. Calculate the mean volume of hydrogen produced. Give your answer to 3 significant figures.

	Repeat 1	Repeat 2	Repeat 3
Volume of hydrogen (cm^3)	22.3	24.5	23.9

....

....

.... cm^3

[2]

2. The number of C and H atoms in four different hydrocarbons is shown on the chart below.
As shown on the chart, the ratio of C : H atoms in methane is 1 : 4.
The ratio of C : H atoms in one of the other hydrocarbons is 1 : 3 in its simplest form.
Identify which hydrocarbon has this ratio of atoms.

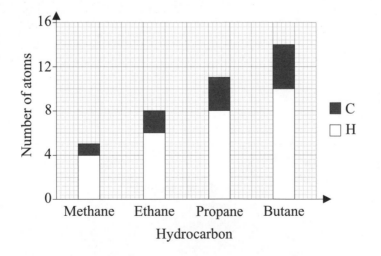

....

....

....

[2]

© CGP — not to be photocopied

The graph below shows the mass of a gas product lost from a reaction vessel in 100 seconds.

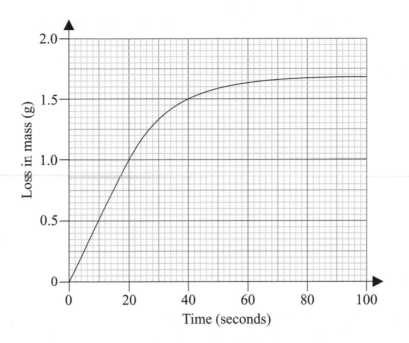

3. Calculate the amount of mass lost from the reaction vessel between 20 seconds and 40 seconds.

....

.... g

[1]

4. Use your answer from question 3, and the following formula to calculate the mean rate of reaction between 20 seconds and 40 seconds. Include the units for the rate in your answer.

$$\text{mean rate of reaction} = \frac{\text{change in } y}{\text{change in } x}$$

....

....

....

[3]

8

Chemistry: Test 9

There are **5 questions** in this test. Give yourself **10 minutes** to answer them all.

1. The following rule always applies to chemical reactions:

    mass of reactants = mass of products

    135.6 g of aluminium reacts with some oxygen to produce 256.1 g of aluminium oxide.
    Aluminium and oxygen are the reactants. Aluminium oxide is the only product.
    Calculate the mass of oxygen involved in this reaction.

    ....

    .... g
    [1]

2. An atom has a diameter of 1×10^{-10} m. The nucleus of the atom has a diameter of 1×10^{-14} m.
    How many times bigger is the diameter of the atom than the diameter of its nucleus?

    ....

    ....

    ....
    [2]

3. 24 g of salt is dissolved in water to make a solution with a concentration of 1.6 g/dm³.
    Using the formula below, calculate the volume of water used to make the solution.

    $$\text{concentration (g/dm}^3) = \frac{\text{mass (g)}}{\text{volume (dm}^3)}$$

    ....

    ....

    .... dm³
    [3]

© CGP — not to be photocopied

The graph below shows how the concentration of a reactant changes during a reaction.

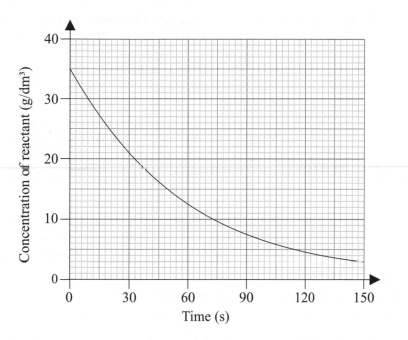

4. Calculate the decrease in the concentration of the reactant between 30 and 60 s.

....

....

.... g/dm³

[1]

5. Use your answer to question 4 to calculate the mean rate of reaction between 30 and 60 s.

$$\text{mean rate of reaction} = \frac{\text{change in concentration of reactant}}{\text{time taken}}$$

....

....

.... g/dm³/s

[2]

9

Chemistry: Test 10

There are **5 questions** in this test. Give yourself **10 minutes** to answer them all.

1. Naazira recorded the change in mass of reactants in an experiment. She repeated the experiment four times and calculated a mean. Her results are shown in the table below.
    Calculate the mean of the results in the table.

	Repeat 1	Repeat 2	Repeat 3	Repeat 4
Change in mass (g)	2.37	2.41	2.63	2.59

....

.... g

[1]

A scientist measured the level of air pollution in a city over 5 years.
The data the scientist collected is shown in the table below.

Year	2009	2010	2011	2012	2013
Mean air pollution ($\mu g/m^3$)	97	110	122	91	102

2. Draw a bar chart of the data in the table on the axes below.

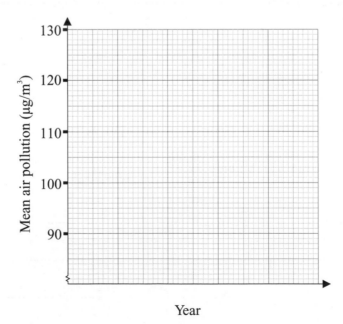

[2]

© CGP — not to be photocopied

3. The mean air pollution in the city was 5% higher in 2014 than 2013.
    Calculate the mean air pollution in 2014.

    ....

    ....

    ....μg/m³

    [2]

4. In 2012, the mean air pollution was found to contain a 2 : 5 ratio of sulfur dioxide : other
    pollutants. Calculate the level of sulfur dioxide in the air in 2012.

    ....

    ....

    .... μg/m³

    [2]

5. The diagram below represents a nanoparticle. Its dimensions are given in nanometres (nm).
    Calculate the surface area of this nanoparticle. Give your answer to 3 significant figures.

    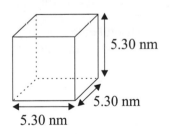

    5.30 nm

    5.30 nm

    5.30 nm

    ....

    ....

    .... nm²

    [2]

    9

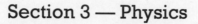

Physics: Test 1

There are **5 questions** in this test. Give yourself **10 minutes** to answer them all.

1. A current of 4.80 A flows through a resistor. The resistor has a resistance of 3.50 Ω.
    Calculate the potential difference across the resistor. Use the formula:

    $$V = IR$$

    Where:
    * V is the potential difference in V,
    * I is the current in A,
    *   and R is the resistance in Ω.

    ....

    ....

    V

    [2]

2. A motor has an efficiency of 0.75.
    The input energy transfer to the motor is 2.4 J.
    Calculate the useful output energy transfer of the motor.

    $$\text{efficiency} = \frac{\text{useful output energy transfer}}{\text{total input energy transfer}}$$

    ....

    ....

    ....

    .... J

    [3]

                                          © CGP — not to be photocopied

The graph below shows how the activity of a sample of a radioactive isotope changes over time.

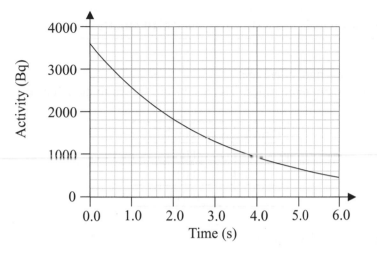

3. The half-life of a radioactive substance is the time taken for the activity to halve.
Use the graph to calculate the half-life of the radioactive isotope.

....

....

.... s

[2]

4. How long does it take for the activity shown in the graph to drop below 1000 Bq?

.... s

[1]

5. Which of the following is equal to 0.00000025 A? Tick **one** box.

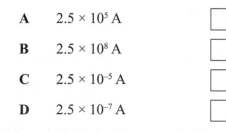

A 2.5×10^5 A

B 2.5×10^8 A

C 2.5×10^{-5} A

D 2.5×10^{-7} A

[1]

$\dfrac{}{9}$

Physics: Test 2

There are **5 questions** in this test. Give yourself **10 minutes** to answer them all.

Rajesh measured the side length of a cube.
He repeated the measurement three times. His results are shown in the table below.

Repeat	Side length (m)
1	0.009
2	0.010
3	0.011

1. Calculate the mean side length of the cube.

    ....

    .... m

    [1]

2. Use your answer to question 1 to calculate the volume of the cube.

    ....

    .... m^3

    [1]

3. The mass of another cube is 0.102 kg. Its volume is 0.001 m^3.
    Use the formula below to calculate the density of this cube.
    Give your answer to 2 significant figures.

    $$\rho = \frac{m}{V}$$

    Where ρ = density in kg/m^3, m = mass in kg and V = volume in m^3.

    ....

    ....

    .... kg/m^3

    [3]

© CGP — not to be photocopied

4. A car battery has a potential difference of 12.6 V.
The battery supplies a current of 65.0 A in order to start the car.
Calculate the power of the car battery when starting the car. Give your answer in kW.

power (W) = potential difference (V) × current (A)

....

....

.... kW

[3]

5. The graph below shows how the weight of an object changes with its
mass on three different planets.

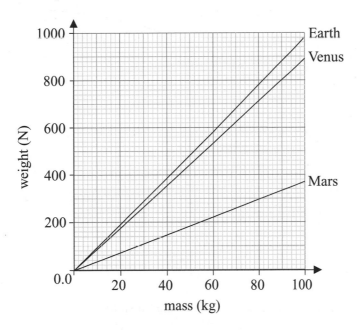

Weight and mass are linked by the formula:

gravitational field strength = weight ÷ mass

Using this information, which of the planets on the graph above has the highest gravitational
field strength?

....

....

[1]

9

© CGP — not to be photocopied   **Physics:** Test 2

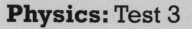

Physics: Test 3

There are **5 questions** in this test. Give yourself **10 minutes** to answer them all.

A racing car crosses a finish line. The graph below shows how the distance from the finish line changes after the car crosses the line.

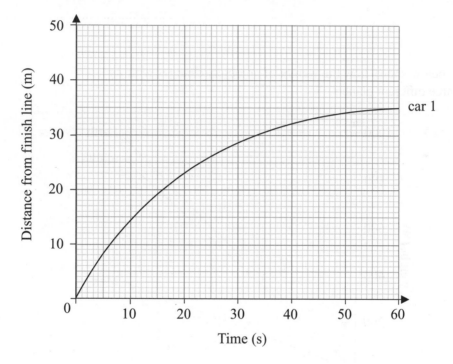

A second car is parked next to the track, 30 m from the finish line.
It is parked there for the same length of time that car 1 is moving.

1. Draw a line on the graph above for the second car.

[1]

2. At what time does car 1 pass car 2?

.... s
[1]

  © CGP — not to be photocopied

A wooden ball is attached to a spring. The mass of the wooden ball is 0.50 kg and the extension of the spring is 0.098 m.
The gravitational field strength is 9.8 N/kg.

3. Calculate the weight of the wooden ball.

weight (N) = mass (kg) × gravitational field strength (N/kg)

....

....

.... N

[2]

4. The weight of the wooden ball is equal to the force on the spring. Use your answer to question 3 and the formula below to calculate the spring constant of the spring.

force (N) = spring constant (N/m) × extension (m)

....

....

....

.... N/m

[3]

5. Chloe investigated how the extension of a spring depended on the force on the spring.
She used her results to calculate the energy in the elastic potential energy stores of the spring.
The table on the right shows her results.

Which of the following statements is true?
Tick **one** box.

Weight (N)	Extension (m)	Elastic potential energy (J)
100	0.1	5
200	0.2	20
300	0.3	45
400	0.4	80

A   weight ∝ extension ☐

B   extension ∝ elastic potential energy ☐

C   weight ∝ elastic potential energy ☐

[1]

8

Physics: Test 4

There are **5 questions** in this test. Give yourself **10 minutes** to answer them all.

1. A sound wave has a frequency of 22 Hz and a wavelength of 15 m.
    Calculate the speed of the sound wave.

    speed (m/s) = frequency (Hz) × wavelength (m)

    ....

    .... m/s

    [1]

2. The diagram below shows a ray of light entering a glass block.
    Which of the following angles is equal to 45°? Tick **one** box.

    A   angle of incidence   ☐

    B   angle of refraction   ☐

    C   angle between boundary
            and normal   ☐

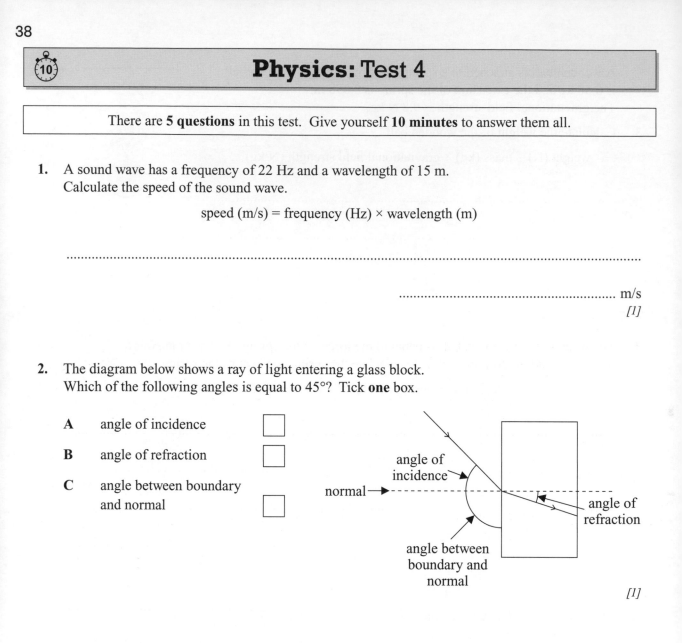

    [1]

3. A moving car has a mass of 1200 kg and has a velocity of 5 m/s.
    Calculate the kinetic energy of the car.

    kinetic energy (J) = $\frac{1}{2}$ × mass (kg) × (velocity (m/s))^2

    ....

    ....

    .... J

    [2]

          © CGP — not to be photocopied

A student heats 0.50 kg of milk using a Bunsen burner. Milk has a specific heat capacity of 3930 J/kg°C. The student uses a thermometer to measure the change in temperature of the milk. The diagram below shows the thermometer before and after the milk was heated.

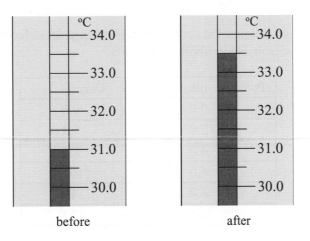

before   after

4. Calculate the change in temperature of the milk during heating.

....

....

.... °C

[2]

5. Use your answer to question 4, and the formula below to calculate the energy transferred to the milk from the Bunsen burner. Assume that no energy is transferred to the surroundings.

energy transferred (J) = mass (kg) × specific heat capacity (J/kg°C) × change in temperature (°C)

....

....

.... J

[2]

8

© CGP — not to be photocopied   **Physics:** Test 4

Physics: Test 5

There are **5 questions** in this test. Give yourself **10 minutes** to answer them all.

A student uses a circuit to measure the current through a lamp for different values of potential difference. The table below shows her results.

Potential difference (V)	Current (A)
0.0	0.0
2.0	5.4
4.0	8.4
6.0	10.2
8.0	11.4
10.0	12.0

The student starts to plot her results on the graph below.

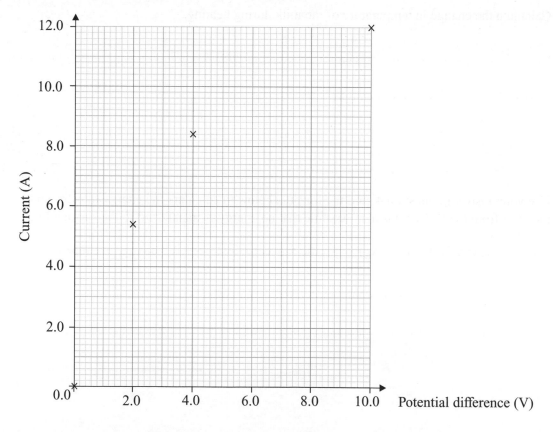

1. Complete the graph by plotting the missing points and drawing a line of best fit.

[2]

© CGP — not to be photocopied

2. Use the graph to estimate the current in the lamp when the potential difference is 5.0 V.

.... A

[1]

3. The student looks at the graph and makes the following statement:

potential difference $\propto$ current

Use the graph to explain why the student is **incorrect**.

....

....

[1]

The gravitational field strength on the moon is roughly $\frac{1}{6}$ of the gravitational field strength on the Earth. The gravitational field strength on the Earth is 9.8 N/kg.

4. Calculate the gravitational field strength on the moon. Give your answer to 2 significant figures.

....

....

.... N/kg

[2]

5. An object on the moon has a weight of 6 N.
Use your answer to question 4 and the following formula to calculate the mass of the object.

weight (N) = mass (kg) × gravitational field strength (N/kg)

....

....

.... kg

[3]

9

Physics: Test 6

There are **5 questions** in this test. Give yourself **10 minutes** to answer them all.

1. The ratio of primary to secondary turns in a transformer is 3:8. The transformer has 120 primary turns. Calculate the number of secondary turns in the transformer.

....

....

.... turns

[2]

The graph below shows how the velocity of an object changes with time.

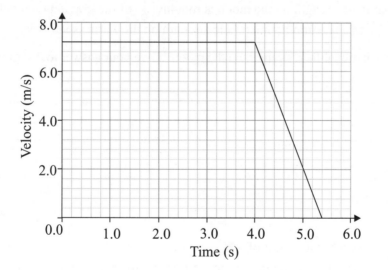

2. The distance travelled by the object is equal to the area under the graph. Calculate the distance travelled by the object in the first 4 seconds.

....

....

.... m

[2]

© CGP — not to be photocopied

3. The gradient of a velocity-time graph is equal to the object's acceleration.
    What is the acceleration of the object at 3.0s?

    .... m/s^2

    [1]

4. The uncertainty in a measurement can be given as a percentage of the amount measured.
    A student measures the uncertainty in the resistance of a wire to be $16 \pm 0.6\ \Omega$. Which of
    the following is equal to the percentage uncertainty in the resistance? Tick **one** box.

    A $16\ \Omega \pm 3.75\ \%$ ☐

    B $16\ \Omega \pm 0.038\ \%$ ☐

    C $16\ \Omega \pm 9.6\ \%$ ☐

    D $16\ \Omega \pm 0.6\ \%$ ☐

    [1]

The table below shows the ranges of frequencies for different colours of visible light.

Colour	Frequency (10^{12} Hz)
Red	400 – 483
Orange	484 – 507
Yellow	508 – 525
Green	526 – 605
Blue	606 – 667
Violet	668 – 788

5. Calculate the period of yellow light at its minimum frequency.

    period (s) = 1 ÷ frequency (Hz)

    ....

    ....

    .... s

    [2]

    8

44

Physics: Test 7

There are **4 questions** in this test. Give yourself **10 minutes** to answer them all.

James is pushing a box along the floor. He applies a force of 5 N to the box over an area of 0.1 m². In doing this, James does 3.5 J of work on the box.

1. Calculate the pressure James applies to the box.   pressure (Pa) = force (N) ÷ area (m²)

    ....

    ....

    .... Pa

    [2]

2. Calculate the distance the box moves. Ignore any frictional forces that may be acting on the box.

    work done (J) = force applied (N) × distance moved (m)

    ....

    ....

    .... m

    [3]

3. Ama applied a potential difference of 1.2 V across a wire and measured the current through the wire. She repeated her measurement three times. Ama's results are in the table below.

	Repeat 1	Repeat 2	Repeat 3
Current (A)	5.7	6.0	6.2

    Calculate the mean current through the wire. Give your answer to 2 significant figures.

    ....

    ....

    .... A

    [2]

                                                © CGP — not to be photocopied

Reaction time is the time it takes for someone to react to a change in their environment.
Reaction times vary from person to person.

Two classes of students measured their reaction times to the nearest 0.1 s.
The table below shows the mean results from each class for male and female students.

Mean reaction time (s)			
Class 1 male students	Class 1 female students	Class 2 male students	Class 2 female students
0.6	0.7	0.5	0.4

4. Use the results from the table to complete the bar chart below.

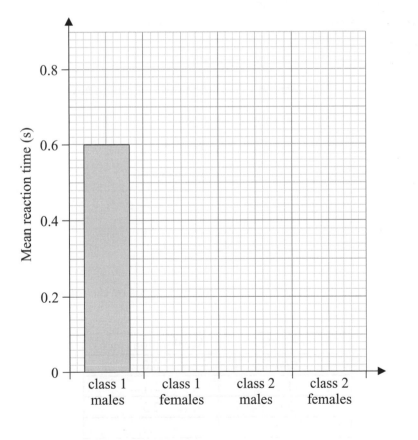

[2]

9

Physics: Test 8

There are **4 questions** in this test. Give yourself **10 minutes** to answer them all.

1. A bike tyre manufacturer states that their tyres should be inflated to a pressure of 690 000 Pa $\pm$ 5%. Calculate the maximum value in this range.

....

....

.... Pa

[2]

2. A spring has a spring constant of 600 N/m.
   When the spring is stretched, the extension of the spring is 0.05 m.
   Calculate the elastic potential energy of the spring.

$$E = \frac{1}{2} \, ke^2$$

Where E is the elastic potential energy in J, k is the spring constant in N/m and e is the extension in m.

....

....

.... J

[2]

A student investigates how the acceleration of a trolley depends on the force applied to the trolley. The table below shows his results.

Force (N)	Acceleration (m/s^2)
0.0	0.0
1.0	1.1
2.0	2.3
3.0	3.4
4.0	4.6

© CGP — not to be photocopied

3. Use the data from the table to complete the graph below. Draw a line of best fit.

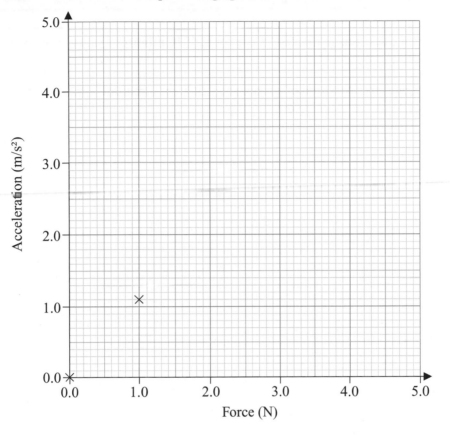

Acceleration (m/s²) vs Force (N)

[2]

4. At a force of 3.0 N, the acceleration of the trolley is 3.4 m/s².
Use this information and the formula below to calculate the mass of the trolley.
Give your answer to 2 significant figures.

$$m = \frac{F}{a}$$

Where m is the mass in kg, F is the force in N and a is the acceleration in m/s².

....

....

....

.... kg

[3]

9

Physics: Test 9

There are **4 questions** in this test. Give yourself **10 minutes** to answer them all.

A student investigates the extension of a rope when different forces are applied to it.
She plots her results on the graph below.

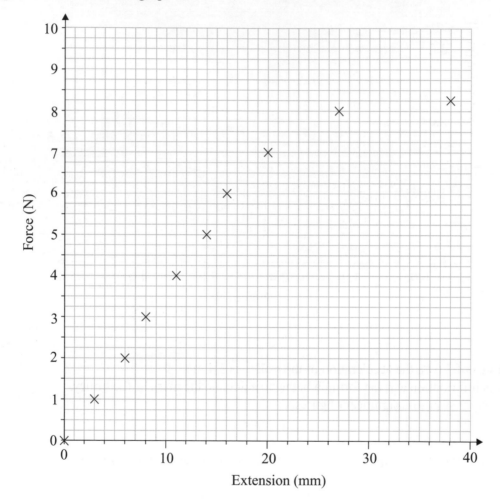

1. Which of the following statements, **A** to **C**, best describes the graph? Tick **one** box.

    A   The relationship between force and extension is directly proportional.

    B   The relationship between force and extension is
            directly proportional only when force is ≥ 7 N.

    C   The relationship between force and extension is
            directly proportional only when force is ≤ 7 N.

    [1]

    © CGP — not to be photocopied

Another student measures how much a spring extends when a force is applied to the spring. He repeats his measurement three times and records the results in the table below.

Force (N)	Extension of spring (cm)		
	1	2	3
3.2	2.8	2.3	2.4

2. Calculate the mean extension of the spring in metres (m).

....

....

.... m

[2]

3. Use your answer to question 2 to calculate the spring constant of the spring.
Give your answer to 2 significant figures.

$$F = ke$$

Where F = the force in N, k = the spring constant in N/m and e = the extension in m.

....

....

.... N/m

[3]

4. An offshore wind turbine has a power output of 2.1 MW.
The input power to the turbine is 3.5 MW.
Calculate the percentage efficiency of the wind turbine.

$$\% \text{ efficiency} = \frac{\text{useful output power}}{\text{total input power}} \times 100$$

....

....

.... %

[2]

8

Physics: Test 10

There are **4 questions** in this test. Give yourself **10 minutes** to answer them all.

A 4500 W water heater is used to heat water for 2.50 minutes.

1. Calculate the energy transferred by the water heater during the 2.50 minutes it is heating for.

    energy (J) = power (W) × time (s)

    ....

    ....

    .... J

    [3]

2. 70% of the energy transferred by the water heater goes towards heating up the water.
   Use your answer to question 1 to calculate how much energy is transferred to heat the water.

    ....

    ....

    .... J

    [2]

3. Tara is measuring the resistance of a resistor.
   She repeats her measurement and records the
   results in the table on the right.
   Calculate the absolute uncertainty of the results.

    absolute uncertainty = range ÷ 2

Repeat	Resistance (Ω)
1	8.6
2	8.9
3	8.7
4	8.4

    ....

    ....

    ± .... Ω

    [2]

© CGP — not to be photocopied

The graph below shows how the current varies with potential difference for
four different electrical components.

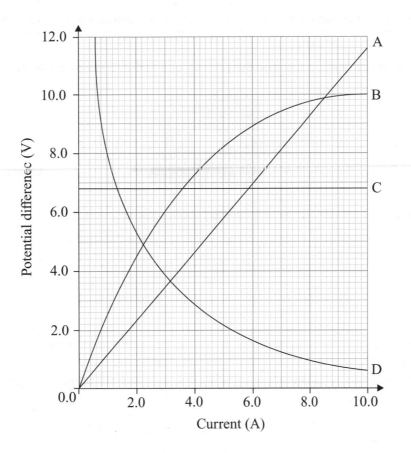

Onc of the components is a resistor. The current and potential difference
in a resistor are directly proportional at a constant temperature.

4. Which of the graphs above, **A-D**, could be for a resistor at a constant temperature?
Tick **one** box.

A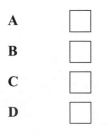

B

C

D

[1]

8

Physics: Test 10

Physics: Test 11

There are **5 questions** in this test. Give yourself **10 minutes** to answer them all.

A step-up transformer has 125 turns on the primary coil and 2750 turns on the secondary coil.

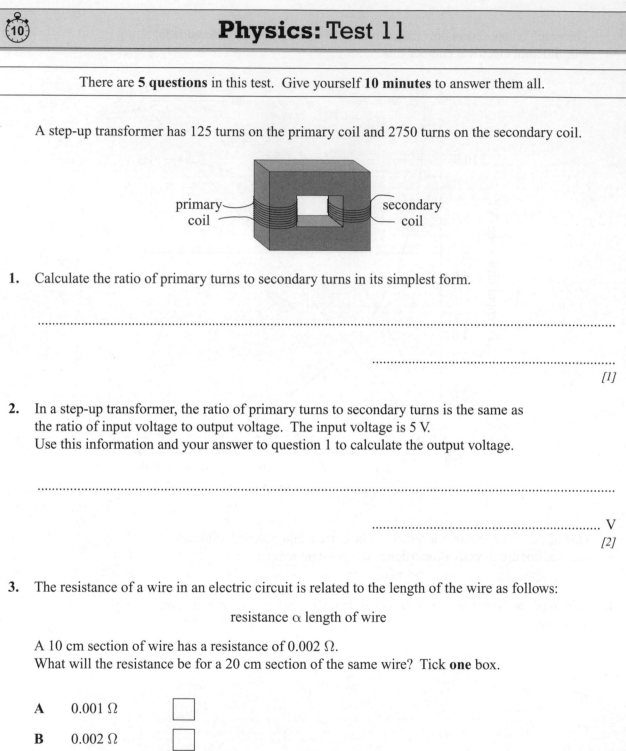

1. Calculate the ratio of primary turns to secondary turns in its simplest form.

   ....

   ....

   [1]

2. In a step-up transformer, the ratio of primary turns to secondary turns is the same as the ratio of input voltage to output voltage. The input voltage is 5 V.
   Use this information and your answer to question 1 to calculate the output voltage.

   ....

   V

   [2]

3. The resistance of a wire in an electric circuit is related to the length of the wire as follows:

   $$\text{resistance} \propto \text{length of wire}$$

   A 10 cm section of wire has a resistance of 0.002 Ω.
   What will the resistance be for a 20 cm section of the same wire? Tick **one** box.

   A   0.001 Ω ☐

   B   0.002 Ω ☐

   C   0.004 Ω ☐

   D   0.008 Ω ☐

   [1]

© CGP — not to be photocopied

4. The graph below shows how the temperature of a solid changes
when energy is transferred to it.

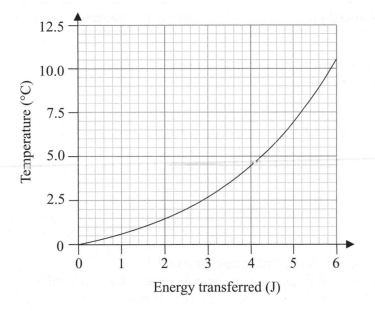

Energy transferred (J)

Calculate the temperature increase when the energy supplied to the solid increases
from 4 J to 6 J.

....

.... °C

[1]

5. The specific latent heat of fusion of water is 334 000 J/kg. Calculate the minimum energy
required to melt a 13.88 kg block of ice. Give your answer to 3 significant figures.

$$E = mL$$

Where E is the minimum energy needed to melt a substance in J, m is the mass in kg,
and L is the specific latent heat of fusion in J/kg.

....

....

.... J

[3]

8

© CGP — not to be photocopied

Physics: Test 11

Physics: Test 12

There are **4 questions** in this test. Give yourself **10 minutes** to answer them all.

1. The work done by an electric heater in 146.4 seconds is 73 200 J.
   Calculate the power of the heater.

$$P = W \div t$$

   Where P is the power in J/s, W is the work done in J and t is the time in s.

....

.... J/s

[2]

2. The graph below shows a velocity-time graph for a vehicle.
   The gradient of a velocity-time graph at any point is equal to the acceleration.
   Use the graph to calculate the acceleration of the vehicle between 10 and 20 seconds.

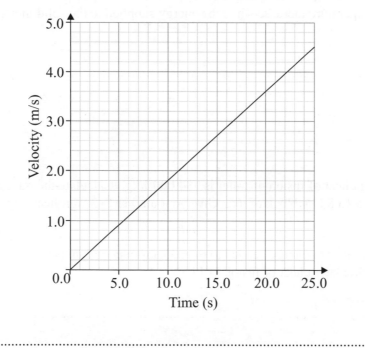

....

....

.... m/s^2

[2]

© CGP — not to be photocopied

A pin is placed on the axis of a converging lens, which acts as a magnifying glass. The scale diagram below shows where the image of the pin is formed when the pin is viewed through the converging lens.

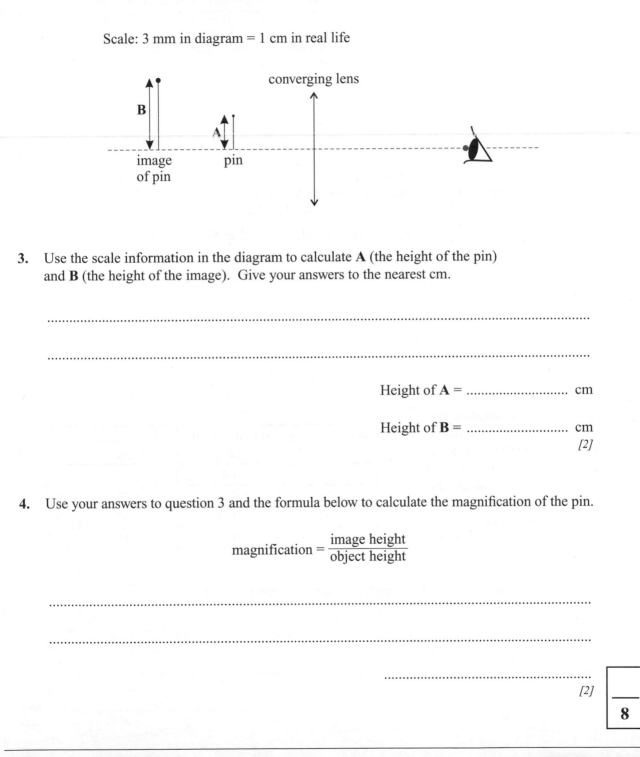

Scale: 3 mm in diagram = 1 cm in real life

3. Use the scale information in the diagram to calculate **A** (the height of the pin) and **B** (the height of the image). Give your answers to the nearest cm.

....

....

Height of **A** = ... cm

Height of **B** = ... cm

[2]

4. Use your answers to question 3 and the formula below to calculate the magnification of the pin.

$$\text{magnification} = \frac{\text{image height}}{\text{object height}}$$

....

....

....

[2]

8

Physics: Test 13

There are **5 questions** in this test. Give yourself **10 minutes** to answer them all.

1. The potential difference across a power line in the national grid is 275 000 V.
    Write this potential difference in standard form.

    V

    [1]

2. A scientist measures the properties of two ocean waves.
    Wave 1 has a wavelength of 120 m and a frequency of 0.1 Hz.
    Wave 2 is moving at $^2/_5$ of the speed of wave 1. Calculate the speed of wave 2.

    speed (m/s) = frequency (Hz) × wavelength (m)

    ....

    ....

    .... m/s

    [3]

A student is investigating how the acceleration of a trolley down a ramp changes when the angle of the ramp is increased. He measures the velocity of the trolley at two points down the ramp, and measures the time taken for the trolley to travel between the two points.

Angle of ramp (°)	Initial velocity (m/s)	Final velocity (m/s)	Time (s)
10	0.41	0.92	0.60
20	0.58	1.38	0.40
30	0.70	1.57	0.35
40	0.79	1.77	0.31

3. Calculate the change in velocity of the trolley when the ramp is at 20°.

    ....

    ....

    .... m/s

    [1]

Physics: Test 13

© CGP — not to be photocopied

4. Use your answer to question 4 to calculate the acceleration of the trolley when the ramp is at 20°.

$$\text{acceleration (m/s}^2) = \frac{\text{change in velocity (m/s)}}{\text{time (s)}}$$

....

.... m/s^2

[2]

5. A motorcycle travels at a constant speed and then begins to decelerate until it comes to a stop. The graph below shows the velocity of the motorcycle on its journey.

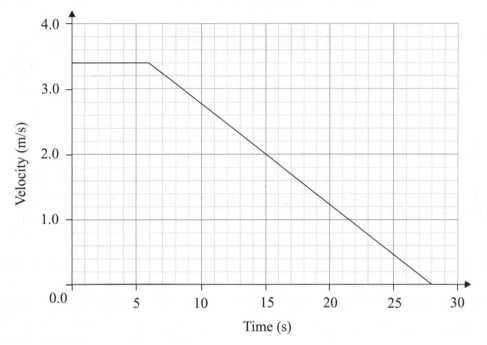

The distance travelled by the motorcycle in metres (m) is equal to the area under the graph. Calculate the distance travelled by the motorcycle between 15 s and 28 s.

....

....

.... m

[2]

9

Physics: Test 14

There are **4 questions** in this test. Give yourself **10 minutes** to answer them all.

1. The diagram below shows a ray of light being reflected off a surface.
   Use a protractor to measure the angle of incidence (*i*).

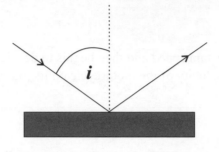

...........................°

[1]

2. A student records the acceleration of a trolley passing through a light gate.
   Her results are shown in the table below. What is the median acceleration of the trolley?

Repeat	1	2	3	4
Acceleration (m/s²)	0.8	0.9	0.8	1.1

....

....

.... m/s²

[2]

3. The wavelength of the waves produced in a ripple tank was measured as 52 mm.
   The frequency of the waves was 5.0 Hz. Calculate the speed of the waves.

   speed (m/s) = frequency (Hz) × wavelength (m)

....

....

.... m/s

[3]

© CGP — not to be photocopied

4. A student carried out an experiment to investigate the properties of a resistor. He measured how the current flowing through the resistor changed with the potential difference. The data in the table shows the results of the experiment.

Potential difference (V)	Current (A)
0.5	0.10
0.8	0.16
1.5	0.30
2.2	0.44
3.3	0.66
4.8	0.96

Use the data to complete the graph below by plotting the missing points.
Draw a line of best fit on the graph.

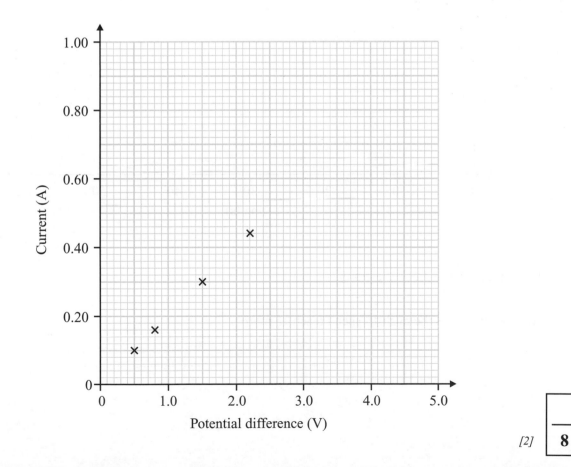

[2]   **8**

Physics: Test 15

There are **5 questions** in this test. Give yourself **10 minutes** to answer them all.

The graph below shows the speed of a cyclist at a number of points during the first 60 seconds of a training ride.

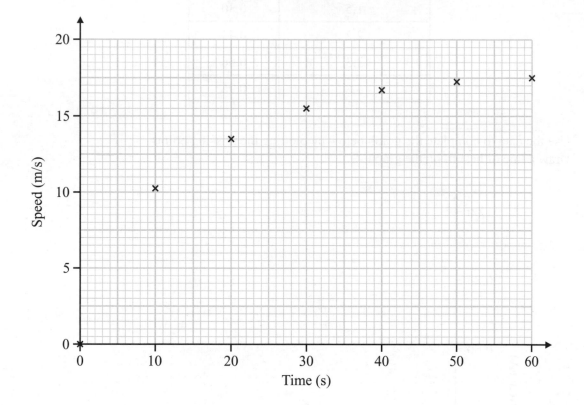

1. Draw a line of best fit on the graph.

[1]

2. At what time does the cyclist's speed reach 15 m/s?

.... s

[1]

© CGP — not to be photocopied

3. A kettle heating element has a resistance of 60 Ω. The current flowing through it is 5 A. Calculate the power of the heating element.

$$P = I^2R$$

Where P is the power in W, I is the current in A, and R is the resistance in Ω.

....

....

.... W

[2]

A new motor is being tested in a factory. The test involves recording the time the motor takes to do 10 000 joules of work. The results of three test runs are shown below.

Test run	1	2	3
Time taken (minutes)	2.25	1.80	2.20

4. Calculate the mean time taken in seconds (s).

....

....

.... s

[2]

5. Use your answer to question 4 to calculate the power of the motor.

$$\text{power (W)} = \frac{\text{work done (J)}}{\text{time (s)}}$$

....

....

.... W

[2]

8

Answers

Section 1 — Biology

Biology: Test 1
Pages 2–3

1. E.g. $63 ÷ 3 = 21$
   $21 × 2 = 42$ cells *[1 mark]*

2. A *[1 mark]*
   Only 1 out of the 4 possible offspring has little wings (nn). So the probability is $\frac{1}{4}$.

3. $BMI = 50.4 ÷ (1.50)^2$
   $= 22.4 \text{ kg/m}^2$
   [2 marks for the correct answer, otherwise 1 mark for $50.4 ÷ (1.5)^2$]

4. E.g.

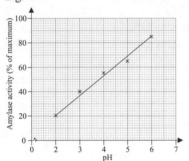

   [2 marks for 3 points correctly plotted, otherwise 1 mark for 2 points correctly plotted. 1 mark for a line of best fit. Maximum 3 marks available.]

5. Mean $= (0.25 + 0.25 + 0.26 + 0.23 + 0.21 + 0.26) ÷ 6 = 0.241... = 0.24$ s to 2 s.f. *[2 marks for the correct answer to 2 s.f., otherwise 1 mark for 0.241...]*

Biology: Test 2
Pages 4–5

1. C *[1 mark]*

2. $A = 27$ mm
   So magnification $= 27 ÷ 0.108$
   $= × 250$
   [2 marks for the correct answer, otherwise 1 mark for $27 ÷ 0.108$]

3. 0.108 mm $× 1000 = 108$ μm
   [1 mark]

4. Volume of water taken up at 2 hours $= 0.6 \text{ cm}^3$
   Volume of water taken up at 6 hours $= 2.1 \text{ cm}^3$
   Change in volume of water $= 2.1 − 0.6 = 1.5 \text{ cm}^3$ *[1 mark]*

5. Time taken $= 6 − 2 = 4$ hours
   Mean rate $= 1.5 ÷ 4$
   $= 0.375 \text{ cm}^3/\text{hour}$
   (or $0.38 \text{ cm}^3/\text{hour}$ to 2 s.f.)
   [2 marks for the correct answer, otherwise 1 mark for correctly calculating the time taken. Allow full marks if incorrect answer to question 4 is used correctly here.]

6. B *[1 mark]*
   Surface area $= (15 × 15) × 6$
   $= 1350 \text{ μm}^2$

Biology: Test 3
Pages 6–7

1. Mean $= (2 + 12 + 7 + 0 + 9) ÷ 5 = 6$
   [1 mark]

2. $4200 × 6 = 25\,200$ bluebells
   [1 mark. Allow mark if incorrect answer to question 1 is used correctly here.]

3. $6.3 \text{ cm}^3 ÷ 54$ minutes
   $= 0.116... \text{ cm}^3/\text{min}$
   $= 0.12 \text{ cm}^3/\text{min}$ to 2 s.f.
   [2 marks for $0.12 \text{ cm}^3/\text{min}$, otherwise 1 mark for $0.116... \text{ cm}^3/\text{min}$]

4.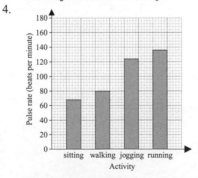

   [2 marks for all 3 bars correctly plotted, otherwise 1 mark for 2 bars correctly plotted]

5. Arrange in numerical order:
   27, 27, 42, 43, 76, 77, 87
   Median (middle number) $= 43$ bacterial colonies *[1 mark]*

6. Mode = the number that appears most often $= 27$ *[1 mark]*

Biology: Test 4
Pages 8–9

1. $625 ÷ 625 = 1$
   $250 ÷ 625 = 0.4$
   So surface area : volume $= 0.4 : 1$
   [1 mark]

2. E.g. the width of the head of the sperm cell fits into the length of the sperm cell approximately 4.5 times. So the width of the head of the sperm cell is approximately:
   $50 \text{ μm} ÷ 4.5 = 11.111... = 11$ μm (accept answers between 10 and 12.5 μm) *[1 mark]*.

3. Cardiac output $= 74 × 70$
   $= 5180 \text{ cm}^3/\text{minute}$ *[2 marks for the correct answer, otherwise 1 mark for the correct calculation]*

4. $1.8 \text{ g} − 2.0 \text{ g} = −0.2$ g
   $(−0.2 ÷ 2.0) × 100 = −10.0\%$
   [2 marks for the correct answer, otherwise 1 mark for the correct calculation]

5. 0.3 mol/dm^3 *[1 mark]*

6. Amount of crop produced in Year 1 $= 7.6$ tonnes
   Amount of crop produced in Year 3 $= 6.2$ tonnes
   $7.6 − 6.2 = 1.4$ tonnes
   [1 mark]

© CGP — not to be photocopied

Answers

Biology: Test 5
Pages 10–11

1. C *[1 mark]*
   A negative correlation means that as one variable increases (e.g. altitude), the other variable decreases (e.g. the number of flowering plant species).

2. real size = $1800 \div 200 = 9$ μm
   [2 marks for the correct answer, otherwise 1 mark for $1800 \div 200$]

3. $(897 \div 9850) \times 100 = 9.1...\%$
   [2 marks for the correct answer, otherwise 1 mark for the correct calculation]

4. Yes, because the pH is greater than 8.8 *[1 mark]*.

5. $105 < h \leq 110 = 5$
   $110 < h \leq 120 = 1$
   Total plants taller than 105 cm = $5 + 1 = 6$ plants
   [2 marks for the correct answer, otherwise 1 mark for the correct calculation]

Section 2 — Chemistry
Chemistry: Test 1
Pages 12–13

1. concentration = $13.2 \div 0.44$
   = 30 g/dm^3
   [2 marks for the correct answer, otherwise 1 mark for the correct calculation]

2. 144 dm^3 × 1000 = 144 000 cm^3
   [1 mark]

3. $(4\ 490\ 000 + 4\ 010\ 000 + 4\ 460\ 000)$
   $\div 3 = 4\ 320\ 000$
   $= 4.32 \times 10^6$ dm^3 per day
   [2 marks for 4.32×10^6, otherwise 1 mark for correctly calculating the mean]

4. C:
   Number of atoms = 3
   A_r × number of atoms = $12 \times 3 = 36$
   O:
   Number of atoms = 1
   A_r × number of atoms = $16 \times 1 = 16$
   [1 mark for both rows of the table correct]

5. A_r × number of atoms for O = 16
   So the percentage mass of O in propanol = $(16 \div 60) \times 100$
   $= 26.66...\% = 27\%$ to 2 s.f.
   [3 marks for the correct answer to 2 s.f., otherwise 1 mark for 26.66...% and 1 mark for the correct calculation. Allow full marks if incorrect answer to question 4 is used correctly here.]

Chemistry: Test 2
Pages 14–15

1. Mass of sodium chloride
   = mass of evaporating dish and contents after heating – mass of empty evaporating dish
   = $26.2 - 25.4 = 0.8$ g *[1 mark]*

2. E.g. convert kg to g:
   1.5 kg × 1000 = 1500 g
   Percentage of carbon in steel alloy
   = $(6 \div 1500) \times 100 = 0.4\%$
   [2 marks for the correct answer, otherwise 1 mark for a correct unit conversion]

3. Repeat 3 =
   (Mean × 3) – Repeat 1 – Repeat 2
   = $(181 \times 3) - 183 - 180 = 180$ s
   [1 mark]

4. E.g.

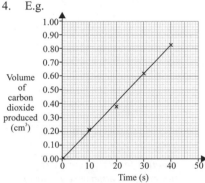

   [2 marks for 5 points correctly plotted, otherwise 1 mark for 4 points correctly plotted, 1 mark for a line of best fit drawn. Maximum 3 marks available.]

5. 0.54 cm^3 *[1 mark — accept answers between 0.52 and 0.54 cm^3]*

Answers

Chemistry: Test 3
Pages 16–17

1. $M_r = 24 + 32 + (16 \times 4) = 120$
   [1 mark]
2. $27 - 25 = 2$
   $(2 \div 25) \times 100 = 8\%$
   [2 marks for the correct answer, otherwise 1 mark for the correct calculation]
3. E.g. convert dm^3 to cm^3:
   $0.200 \ dm^3 \times 1000 = 200 \ cm^3$
   mean rate $= 200 \div 250 = 0.8 \ cm^3/s$
   [3 marks for the correct answer, otherwise 1 mark for correctly converting the units and 1 mark for the correct calculation]
4.
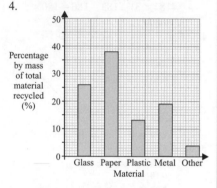
   [2 marks for 4 bars correctly plotted and labelled, otherwise 1 mark for 3 bars correctly plotted and labelled]
5. $1\ 650\ 000 \times 0.26 = 429\ 000 \ kg$
   [1 mark]

Chemistry: Test 4
Pages 18–19

1. The distance from the origin to solvent front $= 4.6$ cm (allow 4.5 cm to 4.7 cm) *[1 mark]*
2. $R_f = 1.4 \div 4.6 = 0.3043...$
   (or 0.30 to 2 s.f.) Allow answers between 0.29 and 0.31.
   [2 marks for the correct answer, otherwise 1 mark for the correct calculation]

3. $23 + 35.5 = 58.5$ *[1 mark]*
4. A_r of Na = 23
   % mass $= ((23 \times 1) \div 58.5) \times 100$
   $= 39.316...\%$
   (or 39.3% to 1 d.p)
   [2 marks for the correct answer, otherwise 1 mark for the correct calculation. Allow full marks if incorrect answer to question 5 was used correctly here]
5. Percentage yield =
   $(2.1 \div 2.8) \times 100 = 75\%$
   [2 marks the correct answer, otherwise 1 mark for the correct calculation]
6. Volume $= 8 \times 8 \times 8 = 512 \ nm^3$
   [1 mark]

Chemistry: Test 5
Pages 20–21

1. $24 \times 0.78 = 18.72 \ cm^3$
   (or $19 \ cm^3$ to 2 s.f.) *[1 mark]*
2. Amount of product formed
   $= 0.140 \times 120$
   $= 16.8$ g *[2 marks for the correct answer, otherwise 1 mark for the correct calculation]*
3. Mass at 30 s = 32.0 g
   Mass at 120 s = 28.8 g
   $32.0 - 28.8 = 3.2$ g
   $(3.2 \div 32.0) \times 100 = 10\%$
   [2 marks for the correct answer, otherwise 1 mark for the correct calculation]
4. Rate = gradient = $\dfrac{\text{change in } y}{\text{change in } x}$
   So the units of rate $= cm^3/s$ *[1 mark]*
5. E.g. $200 \ cm^3$ in $dm^3 = 200 \div 1000$
   $= 0.2 \ dm^3$
   Concentration $= 30$ g $\div 0.2 \ dm^3$
   $= 150 \ g/dm^3$
   [3 marks for the correct answer, otherwise 1 mark for correctly converting the units and 1 mark for the correct calculation]

Chemistry: Test 6
Pages 22–23

1. Maximum theoretical mass =
   $(23.4 \div 78.0) \times 100 = 30$ g
   [2 marks for the correct answer, otherwise 1 mark for the correct calculation]
2. From graph:
   Maximum temperature = 70 °C
   Minimum temperature = 24 °C
   $70 - 24 = 46$ °C *[1 mark]*
3. Mass $= 18 \ g/cm^3 \times 0.46 \ dm^3$
   $= 8.28$ g = 8.3 g to 2 s.f.
   [3 marks for the correct answer to 2 s.f., otherwise 1 mark for the correct calculation and 1 mark for 8.28 g]
4. $10 < x \le 50$ *[1 mark]*
5. Number of hydrocarbons with a boiling point greater than 10 °C
   $= 5 + 2 + 3 + 2 = 12$
   [2 marks for the correct answer, otherwise 1 mark for attempting to add the frequencies of the final four classes in the table]

© CGP — not to be photocopied

Answers

Chemistry: Test 7
Pages 24–25

1. $(2 \div 50) \times 100 = 4\%$ *[1 mark]*
2. $(1 \times 40) + (1 \times 12) + (3 \times 16) = 100$
    [1 mark]
3. $56 \text{ cm}^3 \div 40 \text{ s} = 1.4 \text{ cm}^3/\text{s}$
    [3 marks for the correct answer including the correct units, otherwise 1 mark for either 1.4 or cm^3/s, and 1 mark for the correct calculation]
4. E.g.

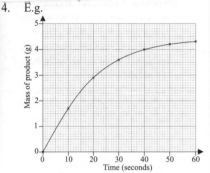

    [2 marks for 4 points correctly plotted, otherwise 1 mark for 3 points correctly plotted. 1 mark for a curve of best fit. Maximum 3 marks available.]
5. E.g. 25 s *[1 mark for correctly reading the graph drawn in Q4 at mass of product = 3.3 g]*

Chemistry: Test 8
Pages 26–27

1. Mean $= (22.3 + 24.5 + 23.9) \div 3$
    $= 23.566... \text{ cm}^3$
    $= 23.6 \text{ cm}^3$ to 3 s.f.
    [2 marks for the correct answer to 3 s.f., otherwise 1 mark for 23.566...]
2. Ethane $= 2 : 6 = 1 : 3$
    Propane $= 3 : 8$
    Butane $= 4 : 10 = 2 : 5$
    So ethane is the only hydrocarbon with this ratio *[2 marks for the correct answer, otherwise 1 mark for evidence of correct ratios derived from the chart]*

3. Loss in mass at 20 s = 1.0 g
    Loss in mass at 40 s = 1.5 g
    $1.5 - 1.0 = 0.5$ g *[1 mark]*
4. Change in y = 0.5 g
    Change in x = 40 – 20 = 20 s
    $0.5 \div 20 = 0.025$ g/s (or 0.03 g/s to 1 s.f.)
    [3 marks for the correct answer including the correct units, otherwise 1 mark for either 0.025 or g/s, and 1 mark for $0.5 \div 20$. Allow full marks if incorrect answer to question 3 is used correctly here.]

Chemistry: Test 9
Pages 28–29

1. $256.1 - 135.6 = 120.5$ g *[1 mark]*
2. E.g. $(1 \times 10^{-10}) \div (1 \times 10^{-14}) = 10\,000$
    or 1×10^4
    [2 marks for the correct answer, otherwise 1 mark for a correct calculation]
3. E.g. rearrange the formula to get:
    volume = mass ÷ concentration
    $= 24 \div 1.6$
    $= 15 \text{ dm}^3$
    [3 marks for the correct answer, otherwise 1 mark for mass ÷ concentration and 1 mark for 24 ÷ 1.6]
4. Concentration at 30 s = 21.0 g/dm^3
    Concentration at 60 s = 12.5 g/dm^3
    $21.0 - 12.5 = 8.5 \text{ g/dm}^3$ *[1 mark]*
5. Time taken = 60 s – 30 s = 30 s
    Mean rate of reaction = $8.5 \div 30$
    $= 0.283...$ $\text{g/dm}^3/\text{s}$ (or 0.28 $\text{g/dm}^3/\text{s}$ to 2 s.f.)
    [2 marks for the correct answer, otherwise 1 mark for ÷ 30. Allow full marks if incorrect answer to question 4 used correctly here.]

Chemistry: Test 10
Pages 30–31

1. $(2.37 + 2.41 + 2.63 + 2.59) \div 4$
    $= 2.5$ g *[1 mark]*
2. E.g.

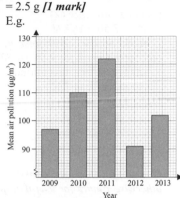
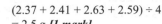
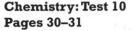

    [2 marks for all 5 bars correctly plotted and labelled, otherwise 1 mark for 4 bars correctly plotted and labelled]
3. E.g. mean air pollution in 2013 = 102 $\mu\text{g/m}^3$.
    5% of 102 = $102 \times 0.05 = 5.1$
    mean air pollution in 2014 = $102 + 5.1 = 107.1$ $\mu\text{g/m}^3$
    [2 marks for the correct answer, otherwise 1 mark for a correct calculation]
4. Total parts in ratio = 2 + 5 = 7
    So one part = $91 \div 7 = 13$ $\mu\text{g/m}^3$
    Amount of sulfur dioxide = $2 \times 13 = 26$ $\mu\text{g/m}^3$ *[2 marks for the correct answer, otherwise 1 mark for the correct calculation]*
5. $5.30^2 \times 6 = 168.54$ nm^2
    $= 169$ nm^2 to 3 s.f.
    [2 marks for the correct answer to 3 s.f., otherwise 1 mark for 168.54]

© CGP — not to be photocopied

Answers

Section 3 — Physics

Physics: Test 1
Pages 32–33

1. potential difference (V)
   = $4.80 \times 3.50 = 16.8$ V
   [2 marks for the correct answer, otherwise 1 mark for 4.80 × 3.50]

2. Rearrange the equation to find the output energy transfer:
   useful output energy transfer
   = efficiency × total input energy transfer
   = 0.75×2.4
   = 1.8 J
   [3 marks for the correct answer, otherwise 1 mark for useful output energy transfer = efficiency × total input energy transfer and 1 mark for 0.75 × 2.4]

3. E.g. the initial activity of the sample is 3600 Bq. After one half-life the activity will be half of this:
   $3600 \div 2 = 1800$ Bq
   Draw a line from 1800 Bq to the curve, and then down to the time axis to find the half-life:

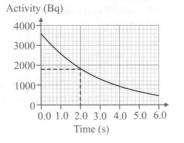

Activity (Bq)

   Half-life = 2.0 s
   [2 marks for the correct answer, otherwise 1 mark for an attempt to read the time taken for the activity to halve off the graph]

4. 3.8 s *[1 mark]*

5. D *[1 mark]*

Physics: Test 2
Pages 34–35

1. mean = $(0.009 + 0.010 + 0.011) \div 3$
   = 0.01 m *[1 mark]*

2. volume = $0.01 \times 0.01 \times 0.01$
   = 0.000001 m³ or
   1×10^{-6} m³
   [1 mark. Allow mark if incorrect answer to question 1 is used correctly here.]

3. density (ρ) = $0.102 \div 0.001$
   = 102 kg/m³
   = 100 kg/m³ to 2 s.f.
   [3 marks for the correct answer to 2 s.f., otherwise 1 mark for 0.102 ÷ 0.001 and 1 mark for 102 kg/m³]

4. power = $12.6 \times 65.0 = 819$ W
   divide by 1000 to convert to kW:
   819 W $\div$ 1000 = 0.819 kW
   [3 marks for the correct answer in kW, otherwise 1 mark for 12.6 × 65.0 and 1 mark for 819]

5. Earth *[1 mark]*
   If gravitational field strength = weight ÷ mass, then the gravitational field strength must be equal to the gradients of the lines on the graph. The line for Earth has the steepest gradient, so Earth has the highest gravitational field strength.

Physics: Test 3
Pages 36–37

1.
Distance from finish line (m)

50
40
30
20
10
0
   10   20   30   40   50   60
            Time (s)

   [1 mark for a straight horizontal line at 30 m]

2. 33 s (allow 33 to 34 s) *[1 mark]*

3. weight = 0.50×9.8
   = 4.9 N
   [2 marks for the correct answer, otherwise 1 mark for the correct calculation]

4. Rearrange the equation to find the spring constant:
   spring constant = force ÷ extension
   = $4.9 \div 0.098$
   = 50 N/m
   [3 marks for the correct answer, otherwise 1 mark for spring constant = force ÷ extension and 1 mark for 4.9 ÷ 0.098. Allow full marks if incorrect answer to question 3 is used correctly here.]

5. A *[1 mark]*
   The symbol '∝' means 'proportional to'. Weight is proportional to extension because as weight increases by a factor, extension increases by the same factor. E.g. as weight increases from 100 N to 200 N (a factor of 2), extension increases from 0.1 m to 0.2 m (also a factor of 2).

Physics: Test 4
Pages 38–39

1. Speed = 22×15
   = 330 m/s *[1 mark]*

2. A *[1 mark]*

3. Kinetic energy = $\frac{1}{2} \times 1200 \times 5^2$
   = 15 000 J *[2 marks for the correct answer, otherwise 1 mark for 1/2 × 1200 × 5²]*

4. The temperature on the first thermometer is 31.0 °C and the temperature on the second thermometer is 33.5 °C.
   Change in temperature = $33.5 - 31.0$
   = 2.5 °C *[2 marks for the correct answer, otherwise 1 mark for 33.5 − 31]*

5. Energy = $0.50 \times 3930 \times 2.5$
   = 4912.5 J (or 4900 J to 2 s.f.)
   [2 marks for the correct answer, otherwise 1 mark for 0.50 × 3930 × 2.5. Allow full marks if incorrect answer to question 4 is used correctly here.]

© CGP — not to be photocopied

67

Answers

Physics: Test 5
Pages 40–41

1. E.g.

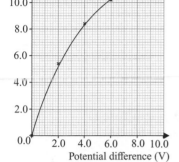

[1 mark for plotting both points correctly and 1 mark for a curved line of best fit]

2. Draw a line from 5.0 V to the curve, and then across to the *y*-axis to find the current.

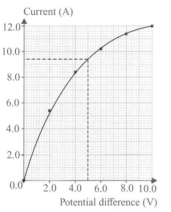

From the graph, current at 5.0 V = 9.4 A *[1 mark for any value between 9.2 and 9.6 A]*.

3. The graph is not linear. If current and potential difference were proportional then the graph would be a straight line (through the origin) *[1 mark]*.

'∝' means 'is proportional to'.

4. The gravitational field strength on the moon = $9.8 \times \frac{1}{6} = 1.633...$ = 1.6 N/kg to 2 s.f.
[2 marks for the correct answer, otherwise 1 mark for $9.8 \times \frac{1}{6}$]

5. weight = mass × gravitational field strength, so mass = weight ÷ gravitational field strength
mass = 6 ÷ 1.6
= 3.75 kg
[3 marks for the correct answer, otherwise 1 mark for mass = weight ÷ gravitational field strength and 1 mark for 6 ÷ 1.6. Allow full marks if incorrect answer to question 4 is used correctly here.]

Physics: Test 6
Pages 42–43

1. $120 \div 3 = 40$
$40 \times 8 = 320$ turns *[2 marks for the correct answer, otherwise 1 mark for $120 \div 3$]*

2.

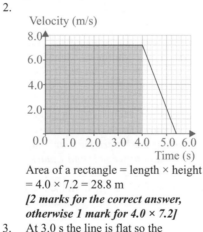

Area of a rectangle = length × height
= 4.0 × 7.2 = 28.8 m
[2 marks for the correct answer, otherwise 1 mark for 4.0 × 7.2]

3. At 3.0 s the line is flat so the gradient is 0.
So acceleration = 0 m/s² *[1 mark]*

4. A *[1 mark]*

5. The minimum frequency in the yellow range is 508×10^{12} Hz, so
period = $\frac{1}{508 \times 10^{12}}$
= $1.968... \times 10^{-15}$ s
(or 1.97×10^{-15} s to 3 s.f.)
[2 marks for the correct answer, otherwise 1 mark for $1 \div (508 \times 10^{12})$]

Physics: Test 7
Pages 44–45

1. Pressure = 5 ÷ 0.1 = 50 Pa
[2 marks for the correct answer, otherwise 1 mark for 5 ÷ 0.1]

2. Rearrange the equation for distance:
distance = work done ÷ force
= 3.5 ÷ 5 = 0.7 m
[3 marks for the correct answer, otherwise 1 mark for correctly rearranging the equation and 1 mark for 3.5 ÷ 5]

3. Mean current = (5.7 + 6.0 + 6.2) ÷ 3
= 5.966... A = 6.0 A (to 2 s.f.)
[2 marks for the correct answer to 2 s.f., otherwise 1 mark for 5.966... A]

4.

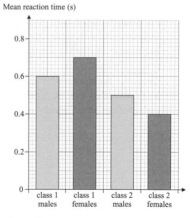

[2 marks for 3 bars plotted correctly, otherwise 1 mark for 2 bars plotted correctly]

© CGP — not to be photocopied

Answers

68

Answers

Physics: Test 8
Pages 46–47

1. E.g. 5% of 690 000 =
   690 000 × 0.05 = 34 500 Pa
   Maximum pressure =
   690 000 + 34 500 = 724 500 Pa
   (or 720 000 Pa to 2 s.f.)
   [2 marks for the correct answer, otherwise 1 mark for a correct percentage calculation]

2. $E = \frac{1}{2} \times 600 \times 0.05^2 = 0.75$ J
   [2 marks for the correct answer, otherwise 1 mark for the correct calculation]

3. E.g.
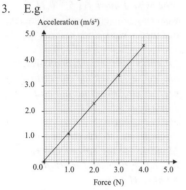
   [1 mark for plotting all 3 points correctly, 1 mark for a line of best fit]

4. *m* (mass) = 3.0 ÷ 3.4 = 0.882... kg
   = 0.88 kg (to 2 s.f.)
   [3 marks for the correct answer to 2 s.f., otherwise 1 mark for the correct calculation and 1 mark for 0.882...]

Physics: Test 9
Pages 48–49

1. C *[1 mark]*
2. Mean = (2.8 + 2.3 + 2.4) ÷ 3
         = 2.5 cm
   2.5 cm in m = 2.5 ÷ 100 = 0.025 m
   [2 marks for the correct answer in m, otherwise 1 mark for 2.5 cm]
3. Rearrange the equation to find the spring constant:
   $k = F \div e = 3.2 \div 0.025 = 128$ N/m
   = 130 N/m to 2 s.f.
   [3 marks for the correct answer to 2 s.f., otherwise 1 mark for correctly rearranging the equation and 1 mark for 128 N/m. Allow full marks if incorrect answer to question 2 is used correctly here.]
4. % efficiency = (2.1 ÷ 3.5) × 100
   = 60% *[2 marks for the correct answer, otherwise 1 mark for the correct calculation]*

Physics: Test 10
Pages 50–51

1. The equation for energy uses the time in s. Multiply the time in minutes by 60 to convert it to s:
   2.50 × 60 = 150 s
   Energy = power × time
          = 4500 × 150 = 675 000 J
   [3 marks for the correct answer, otherwise 1 mark for converting minutes to seconds and 1 mark for 4500 × 150]
2. 70% of the energy from the heater goes towards heating the water:
   0.70 × 675 000 = 472 500 J
   [2 marks for the correct answer, otherwise 1 mark for 0.70 × 675 000. Allow full marks if incorrect answer to question 1 is used correctly here.]

3. Range = highest result – lowest result = 8.9 – 8.4 = 0.5 Ω
   Absolute uncertainty = range ÷ 2
   = 0.5 ÷ 2 = ± 0.25 Ω (or ± 0.3 Ω to 1 s.f.) *[2 marks for the correct answer, otherwise 1 mark for correctly calculating the range]*
4. A *[1 mark]*
   Directly proportional means that as one variable increases (e.g. current), the other variable (e.g. potential difference) also increases at the same rate.

Physics: Test 11
Pages 52–53

1. $\frac{2750}{125} = 22$
   So the ratio = 1 : 22 *[1 mark]*
2. 5 × 22 = 110 V *[2 marks for the correct answer, otherwise 1 mark for 5 × 22. Allow full marks if incorrect answer to question 3 is used correctly here.]*
3. C *[1 mark]*
   'Resistance ∝ length of wire' means that resistance is directly proportional to length of wire. So if the length of the wire doubles, so does the resistance.
4. Temperature at 4 J = 4.5
   Temperature at 6 J = 10.5
   10.5 – 4.5 = 6.0 °C *[1 mark]*
5. Energy = 13.88 × 334 000
          = 4 635 920
          = 4 640 000 J (to 3 s.f.)
   [3 marks for the correct answer to 3 s.f., otherwise 1 mark for 13.88 × 334 000, and 1 mark for 4 635 920]

Answers

© CGP — not to be photocopied

Answers

Physics: Test 12
Pages 54–55

1. Power = 73 200 ÷ 146.4
   = 500 J/s
   [2 marks for the correct answer, otherwise 1 mark for 73 200 ÷ 146.4]

2.
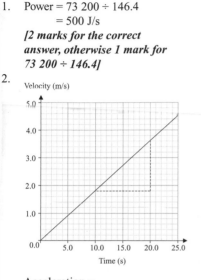

Acceleration =
gradient = $\dfrac{\text{change in } y}{\text{change in } x}$
Change in y = 3.6 – 1.8 = 1.8 m/s
Change in x = 20.0 – 10.0 = 10.0 s
Acceleration = 1.8 ÷ 10.0
   = 0.18 m/s²
[2 marks for the correct answer, otherwise 1 mark for a correct method of calculating the gradient]

3. A measures 9 mm in the diagram. The scale is 3 mm = 1 cm, so the height of A = 9 ÷ 3 = 3 cm *[1 mark]*. B measures around 19 mm in the diagram. The height of B = 19 ÷ 3 = 6.333... cm = 6 cm (to the nearest cm) *[1 mark]*.

4. Magnification = 6 ÷ 3 = 2
   [2 marks for the correct answer, otherwise 1 mark for 6 ÷ 3. Allow full marks if incorrect answers to question 3 are used correctly here.]

Physics: Test 13
Pages 56–57

1. 2.75×10^5 V *[1 mark]*
2. Speed of wave 1 = 0.1 × 120
   = 12 m/s

   The speed of wave 2 is ²⁄₅ of this:
   (12 ÷ 5) × 2 = 4.8 m/s
   [3 marks for the correct answer, otherwise 1 mark for calculating the speed of the wave 1, and 1 mark for (12 ÷ 5) × 2]
3. Change in velocity
   = final velocity – initial velocity
   = 1.38 – 0.58 = 0.80 m/s *[1 mark]*
4. Acceleration = 0.80 ÷ 0.40
   = 2.0 m/s²
   [2 marks for the correct answer, otherwise 1 mark for 0.80 ÷ 0.40. Allow full marks if incorrect answer to question 3 is used correctly here.]
5. E.g.
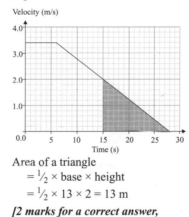
   Area of a triangle
   = ¹⁄₂ × base × height
   = ¹⁄₂ × 13 × 2 = 13 m
   [2 marks for a correct answer, otherwise 1 mark for ¹⁄₂ × 13 × 2]

Physics: Test 14
Pages 58–59

1. 55° *[1 mark]*
2. Arrange the data in order of size:
   0.8, 0.8, 0.9, 1.1.
   There's an even number of values, so the median is halfway between the two middle values:
   0.9 + 0.8 = 1.7
   1.7 ÷ 2 = 0.85 m/s²
   [2 marks for the correct answer, otherwise 1 mark for indicating that the median is halfway between 0.8 and 0.9]
3. 52 mm = 52 ÷ 1000 = 0.052 m
   speed = frequency × wavelength
   = 5.0 × 0.052 = 0.26 m/s
   [3 marks for the correct answer, otherwise 1 mark for correctly converting 52 mm to metres and 1 mark for 5 × 0.052]
4.
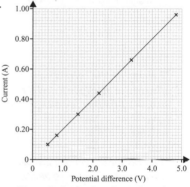
   [1 mark for both points plotted correctly, plus 1 mark for a correct line of best fit]

© CGP — not to be photocopied

Answers

Physics: Test 15
Pages 60–61

1.
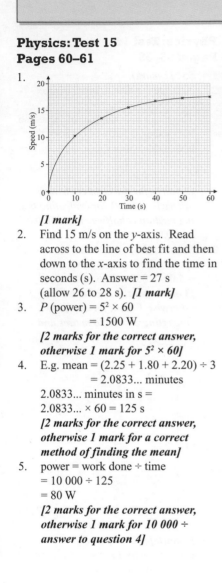

[1 mark]

2.   Find 15 m/s on the *y*-axis. Read across to the line of best fit and then down to the *x*-axis to find the time in seconds (s). Answer = 27 s (allow 26 to 28 s). *[1 mark]*

3. P (power) = $5^2 \times 60$
            = 1500 W
     [2 marks for the correct answer, otherwise 1 mark for $5^2 \times 60$]

4.   E.g. mean = $(2.25 + 1.80 + 2.20) \div 3$
            = 2.0833... minutes
     2.0833... minutes in s =
     2.0833... $\times$ 60 = 125 s
     [2 marks for the correct answer, otherwise 1 mark for a correct method of finding the mean]

5.   power = work done $\div$ time
            = 10 000 $\div$ 125
            = 80 W
     [2 marks for the correct answer, otherwise 1 mark for 10 000 $\div$ answer to question 4]

© CGP — not to be photocopied

SMFXP41